Oxford Read and Imagine

The Cake Machine

By Paul Shipton

Illustrated by Steve Cox

Activities by Hannah Fish

Contents

OXFORD
UNIVERSITY PRESS

Grandpa and Clunk go to the store in the van.

Grandpa looks for eggs and milk.

'Can you see strawberries, Clunk?' he asks.

In the kitchen, Ben and Rosie see the shopping bags.

'Do you like cake?' asks Grandpa.

'Yes!' say Ben and Rosie.

Do you like cake?

→ Go to page 15 for activities.

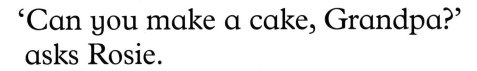

'Can you make a cake, Grandpa?' asks Rosie.

'Yes, I can,' says Grandpa. 'This is my new machine. It's a Cake Machine!'

It's a Cake Machine!

Grandpa puts eggs, flour, and butter in the machine.

Then Clunk puts in sugar and strawberries.

Grandpa counts, 'Three, two, one ...'

→ Go to page 16 for activities.

'A big, red cake!' says Grandpa.

A cake comes out. It isn't big and red.

It's small and black.

'We can't eat this!' says Ben.

'Let's make a new cake,' says Grandpa.
Ben and Rosie watch the Cake Machine.

→ Go to page 17 for activities.

'Three, two, one ...' Grandpa counts.

There is no cake.

'Where is it?' asks Ben.

Grandpa looks at the machine.

He hits it with his hand.

Where is it?

Then ...
'Here's the cake!' says Clunk.

Here's the cake!

→ Go to page 18 for activities.

11

Mom, Ben, and Rosie go to a café.

They have a big, red, strawberry
ice cream cake!

Grandpa and Clunk don't go to the café.

They're in the kitchen.

'I like this cake!' says Clunk.

I like this cake!

→ Go to page 19 for activities.

Activities before you read

Talk **Look at the front cover of this book. Answer the questions and talk to a friend.**

1 What can you see?

2 How many children are there?

3 Where are they?

4 Do you like cake?

1 **Match.**

1 cake

2 eat

3 machine

4 count

5 hand

6 hit

Activities for pages 4–5

1 Put a tick (✓) or a cross (✗) in the box.

1 This is a store. ✓

2 This is a cake. ☐

3 This is milk. ☐

4 This is a kitchen. ☐

2 Match.

1 Grandpa and Clunk	for eggs and milk.
2 Grandpa looks	'Do you like cake?'
3 Ben and Rosie	go to the store.
4 Grandpa asks,	see the shopping bags.

Activities for pages 6–7

1 **Write the words.**

 **1** _flour_
l r f u o

 **2** _____
g r u s a

 **3** _____
g e g

 **4** _____
t b u t e r

2 **Write *yes* or *no*.**

1 Grandpa has a Cake Machine. ___yes___

2 Grandpa can make a cake. _____

3 Rosie puts flour in the machine. _____

4 Clunk puts in strawberries. _____

5 Grandpa counts. _____

Talk **Can you make a cake? Talk to a friend.**

Activities for pages 8-9

1 Circle the correct words.

1 A cake comes **in** / **out**.

2 The cake **isn't** / **aren't** big and red.

3 The cake is small **the** / **and** black.

4 'We can't **eat** / **make** this!' says Ben.

5 'Let's make a **new** / **old** cake,' says Grandpa.

6 Ben and Rosie **watch** / **watches** the machine.

2 Look at the picture on page 8. Write *yes* or *no*.

1 There are three children. _no_

2 The cake is small. _____

3 The cake is black. _____

4 The Cake Machine is red. _____

5 Clunk has an egg. _____

Activities for pages 10–11

1 Write the words.

1 _____
c o n t u

2 _____
n h d a

3 _____
c h a m i n e

4 _____
t j h

2 Trace the words. Then complete the sentences.

looks ~~counts~~ **hits** **says**

1 Grandpa _counts_ , 'Three, two, one…'

2 Grandpa _____ at the machine.

3 Grandpa _____ the machine with his hand.

4 'Here's the cake!' _____ Clunk.

Activities for pages 12–13

1 Match.

- **1** ice cream
- **2** strawberries
- **3** kitchen

2 Order the words.

1 and / go to / Rosie / a café. / Mom, Ben,

Mom, Ben, and Rosie go to a café.

2 cake. / a / strawberry / have / They

_____

3 the kitchen. / Grandpa and / are in / Clunk

_____

4 like / cake! / I / this

_____

Talk **Do you like this story? Talk to a friend.**

Project My Cake!

1 Complete the chart.

~~pink~~ ~~butter~~ yellow eggs flour
black ice cream blue milk red
strawberries sugar white

Food	Colors
butter	pink

2 Do you know more food and color words? Write them in the chart.

3 Draw your own cake.

4 Write some sentences about your cake. Use the words in the chart to help you.

Talk Talk to a friend about your cake.

Picture Dictionary

ask

butter

café

cake

count

eat

egg

flour

hand

hit

ice cream

kitchen

look for

machine

milk

shopping
bags

store

strawberries

sugar

van

Oxford Read and Imagine

Oxford Read and Imagine graded readers are at eight levels (Starter, Beginner, and Levels 1 to 6) for students from age 4 and older. They offer great stories to read and enjoy.

Activities provide Cambridge Young Learner Exams preparation. See Key below.

At Levels 1 to 6, every storybook reader links to an **Oxford Read and Discover** non-fiction reader, giving students a chance to find out more about the world around them, and an opportunity for Content and Language Integrated Learning (CLIL).

For more information about **Read and Imagine**, and for Teacher's Notes, go to www.oup.com/elt/teacher/readandimagine

For a free Audio download of the story in a choice of American and British English, go to www.oup.com/elt/readandimagine

KEY Activity supports Cambridge Young Learner Starters Exam preparation

OXFORD
UNIVERSITY PRESS

Great Clarendon Street, Oxford, OX2 6DP, United Kingdom

Oxford University Press is a department of the University of Oxford. It furthers the University's objective of excellence in research, scholarship, and education by publishing worldwide. Oxford is a registered trade mark of Oxford University Press in the UK and in certain other countries

© Oxford University Press 2014

The moral rights of the author have been asserted

First published in 2014

2018 2017 2016 2015 2014

10 9 8 7 6 5 4 3 2 1

ISBN: 978 0 19 472225 4

Printed in China

This book is printed on paper from certified and well-managed sources

ACKNOWLEDGEMENTS

Main illustrations by: Steve Cox.

Activity illustrations by: Dusan Pavlic/Beehive Illustration, Alan Rowe, Mark Ruffle.